# My D
# Holiday

Written and illustrated by

## Alix Wood

ISBN 978 185022 235 4

Published by Truran,
Goonance, Water Lane, St Agnes, Cornwall TR5 0RA

Truran is an imprint of Truran Books Ltd
www.truranbooks.co.uk

© Alix Wood, 2011   www.alixwood.co.uk

Printed and bound in Cornwall by R Booth Ltd,
The Praze, Penryn TR10 8AA

# About me

Name

Age

Home town

Hobbies

Favourite food

Favourite colour

Favourite animal

Favourite tv programme

Best friend

Why not keep a holiday diary on the special pages in this book. It will remind you of all the things you did and be a fun souvenir.

# My companions

Who is on holiday with you? Draw them here. You could draw your pets, or even your favourite toys, too.

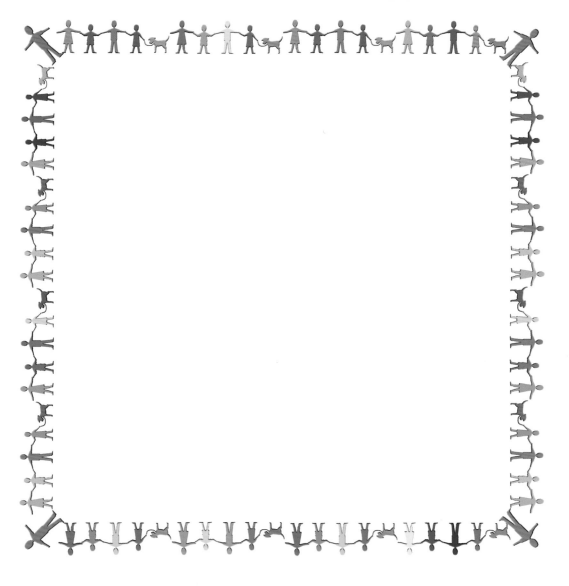

On holiday with me is...

Did you make any friends on holiday?

My friends' names were

My Holiday Diary

# My contacts

Have you contacted anyone
while you were away? How?

| Name of friend or relation | Phoned them? | Texted them? | Sent a postcard? | Other |
|---|---|---|---|---|
| | ☐ | ☐ | ☐ | ☐ |
| | ☐ | ☐ | ☐ | ☐ |
| | ☐ | ☐ | ☐ | ☐ |
| | ☐ | ☐ | ☐ | ☐ |
| | ☐ | ☐ | ☐ | ☐ |
| | ☐ | ☐ | ☐ | ☐ |
| | ☐ | ☐ | ☐ | ☐ |
| | ☐ | ☐ | ☐ | ☐ |
| | ☐ | ☐ | ☐ | ☐ |

You can write some useful numbers and addresses here

## My plans

### Things I'd like to see and do on holiday

My Holiday Diary

# My map of Devon

Here is a map of Devon with some of the big roads and towns on. Do you know where you went on your holiday? You can mark them on the map or make a list of places here.

Ilfracombe
Woolacombe
Braunton
Croyde
Barnstaple
A39
Westward Ho!
Clovelly
Bideford
A39
A386
Meddon
Stibb Cross
Great Torrington
Hatherleigh
Holsworthy
Oak Cross
Okehampton
Lifton
A30
Sourton
Chillaton
A386
Tavistock
Yelverton
Bere Alston
Plymouth
Newton Ferrers

## What was your...    to

longest journey? ..................................

prettiest journey? ..................................

most boring journey? ..................................

wiggliest journey? ..................................

scariest journey? ..................................

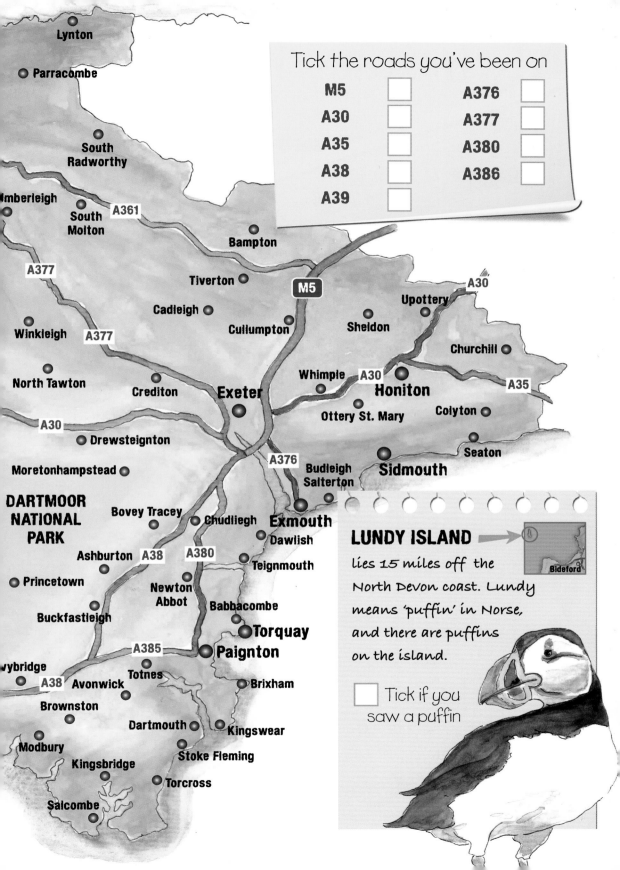

**Tick the roads you've been on**

| | | | |
|---|---|---|---|
| M5 | ☐ | A376 | ☐ |
| A30 | ☐ | A377 | ☐ |
| A35 | ☐ | A380 | ☐ |
| A38 | ☐ | A386 | ☐ |
| A39 | ☐ | | |

Lynton
Parracombe
South Radworthy
Umberleigh
South Molton
**A361**
Bampton
Tiverton
**M5**
Upottery
**A30**
Cadleigh
Sheldon
Churchill
**A377**
Cullumpton
Winkleigh
**A377**
Whimple
**A30**
Honiton
**A35**
North Tawton
Crediton
**Exeter**
Ottery St. Mary
Colyton
**A30**
Drewsteignton
Seaton
Moretonhampstead
**A376**
Budleigh Salterton
**Sidmouth**
**DARTMOOR NATIONAL PARK**
Bovey Tracey
Chudleigh
**Exmouth**
Dawlish
Ashburton
**A38**
**A380**
Teignmouth
Princetown
Newton Abbot
Babbacombe
Buckfastleigh
**Torquay**
**A385**
**Paignton**
Ivybridge
**A38**
Avonwick
Totnes
Brixham
Brownston
Modbury
Dartmouth
Kingswear
Kingsbridge
Stoke Fleming
Salcombe
Torcross

**LUNDY ISLAND** ➔

Bideford

lies 15 miles off the North Devon coast. Lundy means 'puffin' in Norse, and there are puffins on the island.

☐ Tick if you saw a puffin

# My holiday home

Are you in a tent?
Or a caravan?
Or a house?
Or a hotel?

Draw your holiday home here.

## Room checklist

- [ ] bed
- [ ] wardrobe
- [ ] chest of drawers
- [ ] chair
- [ ] carpet
- [ ] mirror
- [ ] sink
- [ ] picture
- [ ] window

What else does
your room have?

# My suitcase

What did you bring with you? Pack this suitcase full of drawings of your stuff.

## Did you need everything?

Are there some things you should have left at home?

........................................................

........................................................

........................................................

Are there some things you forgot?.

........................................................

........................................................

........................................................

........................................................

........................................................

........................................................

........................................................

........................................................

........................................................

........................................................

........................................................

my Holiday Diary

# My journey

## What transport have you used on your holiday?

Give a different colour tick if you have EVER been in any of these.

- train
- car
- motorhome
- boat
- plane
- helicopter
- jetski
- ferry
- bus
- cable car
- coach

- horse
- tractor
- quadbike
- motorbike
- bicycle
- skateboard
- traction engine
- surfboard
- rollerblades
- trike
- scooter

# Car badge bingo

## Cross out the badges when you see them

VOLVO ☐

☐

AUDI ☐

VW ☐

MERCEDES ☐

RENAULT ☐

BMW ☐

VAUXHALL ☐

# My best meal

Draw your favourite meal
that you had on holiday.

## Cream tea wars! How do you like your scone?

The Devon method is to cover with clotted cream, and then top with jam. In Cornwall, it's jam first, then top with clotted cream.

Which do you think works better?

## Food checklist
Tick the foods you like

- apples
- sausages
- nuts
- fish
- bananas
- raisins
- eggs
- bacon
- cheese
- toast
- cereal
- carrots
- chicken
- cake

# My worst meal

Draw your WORST meal here

# Devon spotter game

Here is a list of things you might see on your holiday. You get a point for each one you see. Look out for the bonus points too!

- [ ] Devon flag
- [ ] Sheep
- [ ] Buzzard — **BONUS 10 POINTS**
- [ ] Fishing boat
- [ ] Ice cream van
- [ ] Cream tea
- [ ] The sea
- [ ] Tor
- [ ] Caravan
- [ ] Seal — **BONUS 30 POINTS**

- [ ] South Devon cow — **BONUS 30 POINTS**
- [ ] Seaweed
- [ ] Wild pony — **BONUS 10 POINTS**
- [ ] Gorse bush
- [ ] Castle
- [ ] Thatched cottage
- [ ] Surfer
- [ ] Otter — **BONUS 50 POINTS**
- [ ] Tractor
- [ ] Rainbow — **BONUS 10 POINTS**

**TOTAL**
**154**

1-14 = good  15-35 = well done  36-96 = fantastic
97-120 = wow!  121-154 = unbelieveable!

My Holiday Diary

# My scrapbook page

Here is some space for doodles, writing, lists, and other stuff that will remind you of your holidays. Maybe list the beaches you went to and vote for a winner, or draw some of the most interesting animals you have seen.

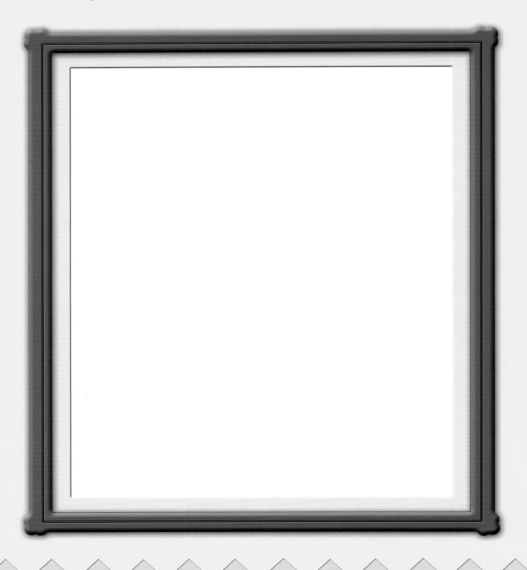

Draw your own postcard

Greetings from Devon

# My weather chart

Here is a chart where you can record the weather for your holiday. Write or draw the weather in the squares. Which was the best day?

## Holiday weather

| Day 1 | Day 2 | Day 3 | Day 4 | Day 5 | Day 6 | Day 7 |
|-------|-------|-------|-------|-------|-------|-------|
|       |       |       |       |       |       |       |

| Day 8 | Day 9 | Day 10 | Day 11 | Day 12 | Day 13 | Day 14 |
|-------|-------|--------|--------|--------|--------|--------|
|       |       |        |        |        |        |        |

# Order your favourite weather from 1-10, 1 for the best, and 10 for worst

| | | | |
|---|---|---|---|
| ☐ | sun | ☐ | warm |
| ☐ | rain | ☐ | hot |
| ☐ | wind | ☐ | hail |
| ☐ | snow | ☐ | thunder |
| ☐ | cold | ☐ | clouds |

# My holiday centre

Where are you staying on your holiday?

- [ ] Village
- [ ] City
- [ ] Holiday Park
- [ ] Town
- [ ] Countryside

You are now entering

_____

Please drive carefully

## Write a poem about it

There was an old man from Bovey Tracey
Who could be incredibly lazy
While picking wild flowers
It took him three hours
To gather just one measly daisy.

_____

_____

_____

_____

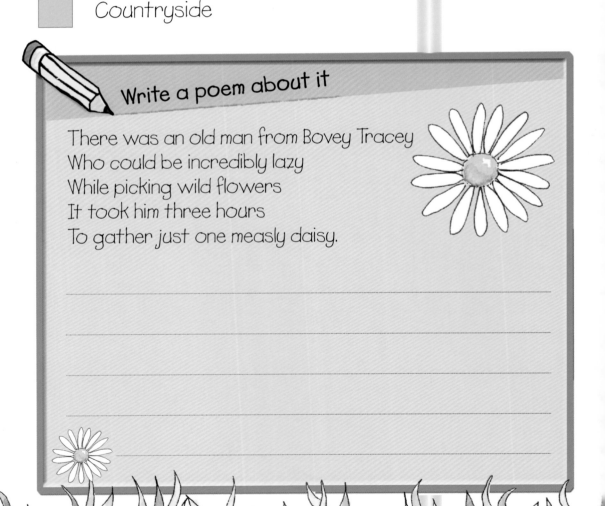

Draw the best flower or the loveliest pebble you found here.

# My Photo album

If you take any photos
stick some here.

My Holiday Diary

# Questionnaire

What was the scariest thing you did?

_____

Did you do anything you had never done before?

_____

What was the funniest thing?

_____

What was the most boring thing?

_____

Who was the grumpiest?

_____

What did you do that you were proudest of?

_____

Did you make friends with any animals?

_____

Have you learnt anything new?

_____

Did you see anything you'd never seen before?

_____

What would you do again if you could?

_____

Did you buy or find any souvenirs that will remind you of your holiday?

DEVON

# Best Place Certificate

This is to certify that

....................................................................................

was the best place I went to on holiday.

Signed

....................................................................................

(Devon Holiday Expert)

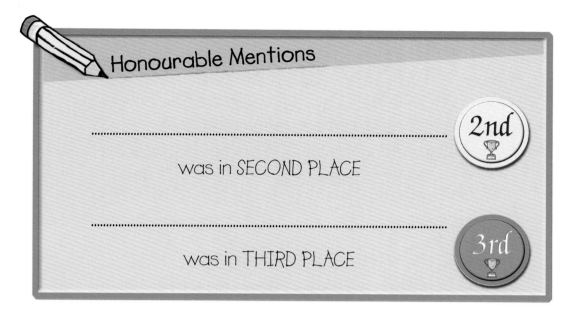

Honourable Mentions

....................................................................... **2nd**

was in SECOND PLACE

....................................................................... **3rd**

was in THIRD PLACE

and in
last place...

The
**Worst Place
on my Holiday
Prize**
goes to

_____

_____

Why?

Did everyone
not like it?

# Holiday review

Give each category a mark out of ten.
Then add them all up to get your **Holiday Score**

| 10 | Companions | 10 | Scenery |
| 10 | Accommodation | 10 | Adventures |
| 10 | Fun | 10 | Things to do |
| 10 | Transport |
| 10 | Food |
| 10 | Friendly people |
| 10 | Weather |

**My Devon Holiday Score is**

**100**

71-100
Top Holiday

41-70
Good Holiday

0-40
Better luck
next time!